A Retina Video Series:

Laser and Cryopexy Techniques

Mandi D. Conway, MD

Assistant Professor of Ophthalmology
Director of Medical Retina and Uveitis
Louisiana State University Eye Center
New Orleans, Louisiana

R. Joseph Olk, MD

Associate Clinical Professor of Ophthalmology
Washington University Department of Ophthalmology and Visual Sciences
St. Louis, Missouri

Williams & Wilkins

BALTIMORE • PHILADELPHIA • HONG KONG
LONDON • MUNICH • SYDNEY • TOKYO

A WAVERLY COMPANY

1995

Williams
& Wilkins

Executive Editor: Darlene B. Cooke
Developmental Editor: Frances M. Klass
Production Coordinator: Marette D. Magargle
Project Editor: Robert D. Magee

A RETINA VIDEO SERIES;
Laser and Cryopexy Techniques
(Complete Set)
ISBN 0-683-02083-8

Panretinal Photocoagulation for Proliferative Diabetic Retinopathy
ISBN 0-683-02084-6

Modified Grid Photocoagulation for Diabetic Macular Edema
ISBN 0-683-02085-4

Laser Treatment of Venous Occlusive Disease of the Retinal Vessels
ISBN 0-683-02086-2

Laser Treatment of Subretinal (Choroidal) Neovascularization
ISBN 0-683-02087-0

Laser Indirect Ophthalmoscopic Treatment of Retinal Disease
ISBN 0-683-02088-9

Transconjunctival Anterior Retinal Cryopexy
ISBN 0-683-02089-7

Williams & Williams
Rose Tree Corporate Center
1400 North Providence Rd., Suite 5025
Media, PA 19063-2043 USA

Printed in the United States of America

Library of Congress Cataloging in Publication Data

94 95 96 97 98
1 2 3 4 5 6 7 8 9 10

Table of Contents

1 PANRETINAL PHOTOCOAGULATION FOR PROLIFERATIVE DIABETIC RETINOPATHY

INDICATIONS, TECHNIQUES, AND COMPLICATIONS OF TREATMENT

Proliferative Diabetic Retinopathy Risk Factors for Severe Visual Loss (According to the Diabetic Retinopathy Study, DRS) include:

1. **Presence** of new vessels (any neovascularization present)
2. **Location** of new vessels
   NVD=Neovascularizationon or within one disc diameter of the optic nerve
   NVE=Neovascularizationon elsewhere in the retina
3. **Severity** of new vessils NVD > standard Photo 10A
4. Vitreous or Preretinal **Hemorrhage**

Indications for treating Proliferative Diabetic Retinopathy

1. Patients with three or four risk factors (According to DRS)–
   Treat Promptly
2. Patients with one or two risk factors (According to DRS)–
   Consider Treatment
3. Patients with severe or very severe nonproliferative diabetic retinopathy–NPDR (According to ETDRS)–
   Consider Treatment in special circumstances

TREATMENT OVERVIEW

1. Initiate treatment with two to three barrier rows placed two to three disc diameters temporal to the fovea.
2. Treat one quadrant at a time starting near the optic nerve and moving outward along the retinal vessels to the periphery.
3. Fill in each quadrant, spacing burns one burn width apart.
4. Fill in the peripheral retina by tilting the lens and using the crescent shaped area in the periphery of the lens to place the burns in the peripheral retina anterior to the equator.
5. If doing a multiple session treatment, try to place the burns in the inferior retina first to avoid delay in treatment in case the vitreous hemorrhage obscures the view prior to the next treatment session.
6. Avoid the direct treatment of major vessels and long posterior ciliary arteries and nerves and elevated NVE.

Techniques

1. Single session PRP
2. Multiple session PRP
3. Supplemental PRP

Single Session PRP

Use 1000 to 1600 burns per session,
determined by type of neovascularization

1000 to 1200 burns per session for NVE alone

1400 to 1600 burns per session for NVD

Multiple Session PRP

Use 500 to 800 burns per session in general

(2-4 sessions spaced at 1-2 week intervals).

Supplemental PRP

For Persistant or Recurrent Neovascularization

Use sufficient burns per session to treat areas of untreated retina and confluent burns to areas of flat NVE.

Anesthesia

1. Topical–prior to retrobulbar
2. Retrobulbar–preferable in most patients
   Use a 50:50 mixture:
   0.75% Marcaine, 2.0% Xylocaine, 150 IU Hyaluronidase (Wydase®)
3. Peribulbar–if monocular
4. General (rarely)–use laser indirect opthalmoscope (LIO).

Laser Wavelength

1. Argon Green (514 nm)
2. Dye (630 or 640 nm)*
3. Krypton Red (647 nm) *
4. Diode (810 nm)

* (Longer wavelengths are useful to treat through vitreous hemorrhages and cataracts.)

Contact Lenses to Use at Slit Lamp

Use lowest magnification on slit lamp.

1. Rodenstock panfunduscopic (This is the lens preferred by the authors.)
2. Quadraspheric (Volk)
3. Mainster wide field lens
4. 3-Mirror Goldmann (It is possible to lose sight of the fovea and inadvertently treat it.)

TREATMENT TECHNIQUES TO USE AT SLIT LAMP

1. Use lowest magnification on slit lamp.
2. Use narrow slit beam of slit lamp.
3. Rodenstock Panfunduscopic (This is the lens preferred by the authors.)–Use 500 μ spot size ~700 μ spot size on retina.

Parameters – Argon Green Laser Treatment

1. 514 nm wavelength (Use in eyes without vitreous hemorrhage or dense cataract.)
2. 200 to 500 micron spot size
3. 0.1 seconds duration (You may use 0.05 seconds in very pain sensitive patients.)
4. 300 to 700 mw average power settings

Parameters – Krypton Red (647 nm), Dye (630 to 640 nm), and Diode Laser (810 nm) Treatments

Use these wavelengths in diabetic eyes with vitreous hemorrhage, cataract, or other media opacity.

1. 200 to 500 micron spot size
2. 0.2 seconds duration (Longer wavelengths may rupture Bruch's membrane more readily. Use longer times and lower power settings to avoid this.)
3. 300 to 700 mw average power settings

TECHNIQUE FOR PANRETINAL PHOTOCOAGULATION FOR PROLIFERATIVE DIABETIC RETINOPATHY.

Step 1: Placement barrier rows temporal to fovea.

Step 1
Begin treatment by placing 2-3 temporal barrier rows 2-3 dd from foveal center. Burns are placed one burn width apart.

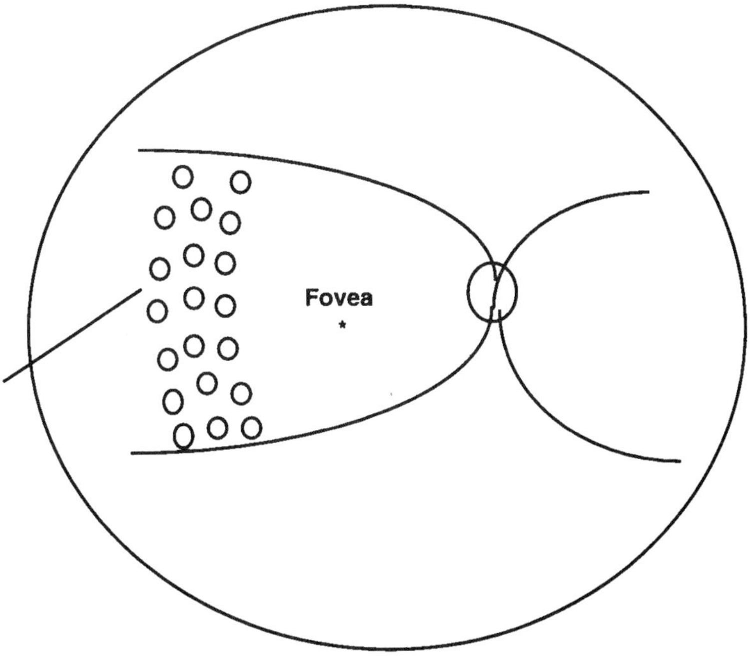

O=500 μ burns placed with Rodenstock Lens are 700 to 750 μ at retina.

Step 1

Treatment is initiated with the placement of two to three rows of burns in an arcuate pattern placed two to three disc diameters temporal to the fovea. This provides a barrier landmark and keeps the laser surgeon from inadvertently treating the fovea. Laser power is titrated during the barrier row placement to achieve a moderately intense white burn. Spots are placed one burn width apart.

Key Points

Place two to three barrier rows to ensure the visibility of the temporal edge of the macular area. These laser lesions are crucial landmarks to assure safe treatment. Take the time to ensure that both you and the patient are seated comfortably without straining at the slit lamp. Get the posterior pole into sharp focus at the beginning of the treatment.

Technique for Panretinal Photocoagulation for Proliferative Diabetic Retinopathy.

Step 2: Beginning treatment peripheral retina.

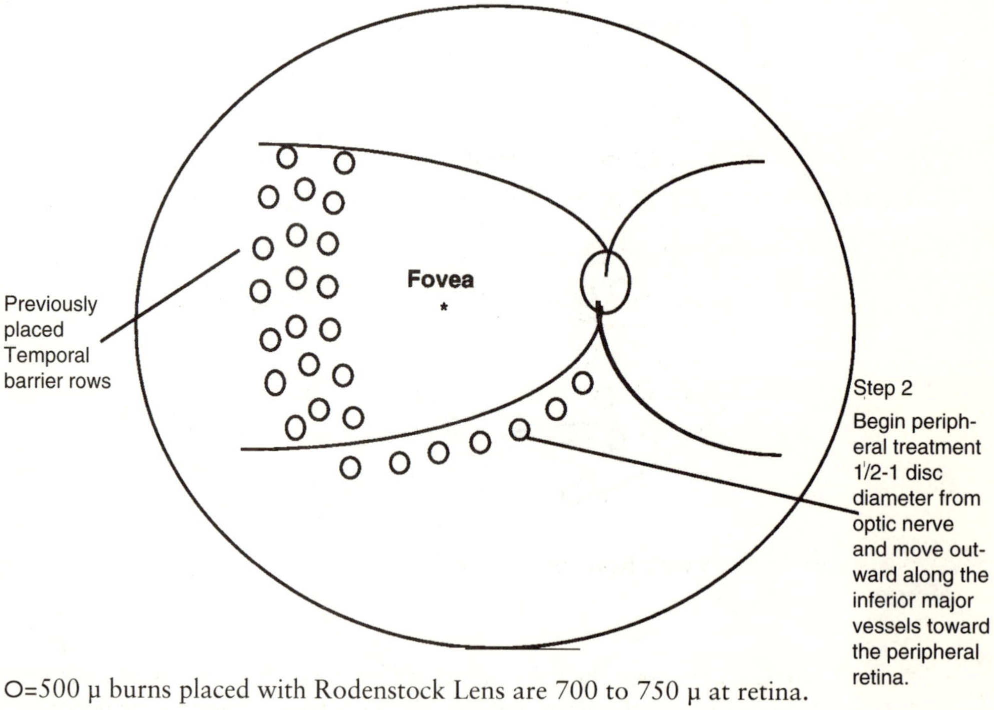

O=500 μ burns placed with Rodenstock Lens are 700 to 750 μ at retina.

Step 2

Following the placement of the temporal barrier rows, begin treating each quadrant starting one-half to one disc diameter from the optic disc and moving outward along the major retinal vessels toward the periphery. Space burns one-half to one burn width from the vessel walls and leave one burn width between burns. Always know the location of the fovea in relation to the area you are treating. If you are not certain, stop and locate the fovea prior to proceeding.

Caution

Avoid direct treatment over the major vessels. If a retinal vessel is inadvertently treated, usually only vasospasm will result, not rupture. It is unusual to cause a complete vascular occlusion during this treatment, but always try to avoid major vessels to eliminate the possibility of a vascular occlusion.

TECHNIQUE FOR PANRETINAL PHOTOCOAGULATION FOR PROLIFERATIVE DIABETIC RETINOPATHY.

Step 3: Completing treatment of inferior peripheral retina.

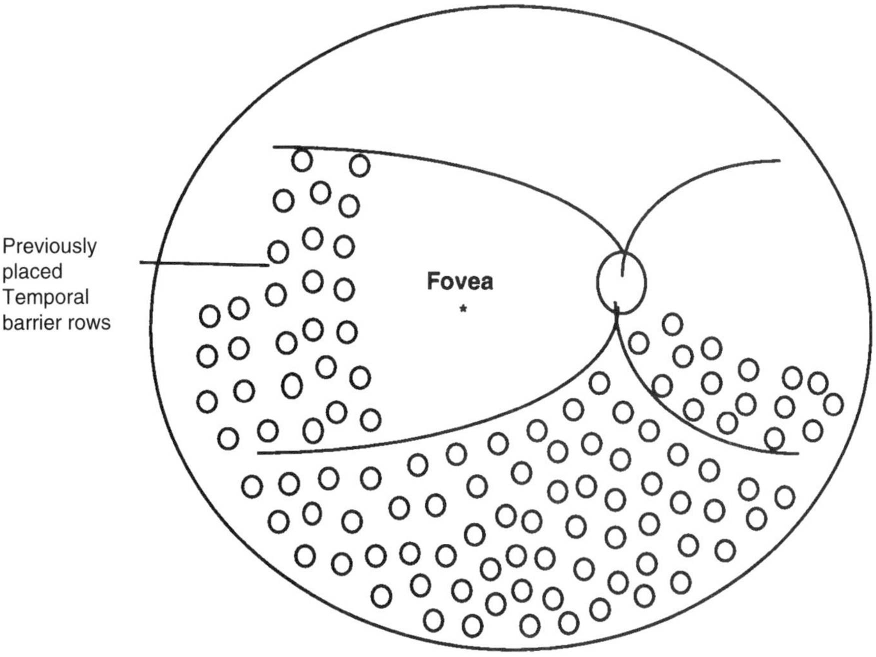

O=500 μ burns placed with Rodenstock Lens are 700 to 750 μ at retina.

STEP 3

If possible, treat the inferior retina first in case the neovascularization bleeds before the second session. When vitreous hemorrhage occurs, gravity will cause blood to collect feriorly, obscuring the view of the retina. Place the burns along the major retinal vessels and space the burns one-half to one burn width from the vessel walls. Leave one burn width between the burns as you move outward to the peripheral retina and fill in the areas between the major retinal vessels. Repeat the treatment, starting near the disc and moving out to the periphery, tilting the lens to the far periphery to focus on one area of the peripheral retina. Adjust the slit lamp as well, to get one crescent-shaped area of retina in focus at a time. Treat all areas of the retina that are in focus and reposition the contact lens to view another contiguous area of the peripheral retina. It will be necessary to readjust the slit lamp to get this next area of peripheral retina into focus. Fill in one quadrant at a time in a systematic manner to insure that there are no areas of the peripheral retina inferiorly that are left untreated.

Technique for Panretinal Photocoagulation for Proliferative Diabetic Retinopathy.

Step 4: Treatment of superior peripheral retina and flat NVE treatment.

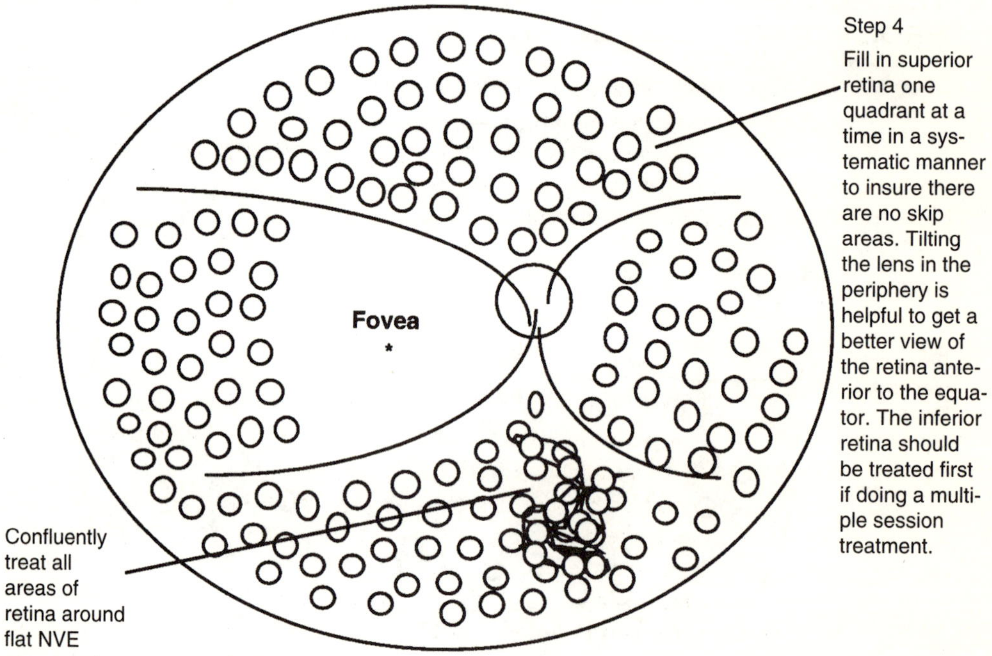

Because the peripheral retina is thin, it is the area wherein a perforation of Bruch's membrane is most likely.

Step 4

As the retina thins in the periphery, the laser power needed to achieve the correct burn intensity may decrease. Tilt the lens in the far periphery to focus on one area of peripheral retina as described previously. Adjust the slit lamp to achieve a sharp focus of one crescent-shaped area at one time and adjust the power to achieve a grey-white burn. To treat another area of the retinal periphery, the slit lamp and the contact lens must be readjusted and refocused. Repeat the treatment from the disc out to the periphery, tilting the lens in the far periphery. Do one quadrant at a time in a systematic manner. Confluently treat all areas of the retina around the flat NVE but not directly over the NVE itself. Scan all areas in the periphery to insure that all areas of the peripheral retina are treated with scatter PRP and all areas of the retina around the flat NVE are confluently treated.

POSTOPERATIVE CARE AND FOLLOWUP

Postoperative Care

If retrobulbar anesthesia is given, the treated eye should have an antibiotic steroid ointment instilled and a patch for four to six hours, until the lid moves. Start topical steroids when the patch is removed (not if the patient is a steroid responder) three to four times daily and continue for five to seven days.

Follow-up

Schedule a postoperative visit in seven to ten days. Watch the IOP carefully. Perform gonioscopy regularly to detect rubeosis. See patient every two to four weeks until regression of proliferative disease occurs. Do a fill-in PRP or transconjunctival anterior retinal cryotherapy for nonregressing neovascularization. (See Tape 6).

Key Points

Place barrier rows initially when a PRP is performed. Note where the fovea is at all times during the treatment. Do no treat directly over areas with elevated neovascularization, since treating these areas will cause vitreous contraction. One may confluently treat areas of the retina around flat NVE. Avoid direct treatment to the major retinal vessels and inside the major arcades. Keep the slit lamp on the lowest magnification for the best view of the peripheral retina. Tilt the lens to view the peripheral retina anterior to the equator. If possible, treat the inferior retina initially to insure that it is adequately treated in case a vitreous hemorrhage occurs before the second session is completed. Treat all areas of the peripheral retina with a "scatter" treatment and areas of the retina around a flat NVE with a confluent treatment.

COMPLICATIONS OF PRP FOR PROLIFERATIVE DIABETIC RETINOPATHY

A. **Poor overview of Retinal Topography or Poor visualization of Landmarks**
   Foveal photocoagulation

B. **Incorrect Focus**
   1. Corneal Burns
   2. Lenticular Burns
   3. Treatment over Long Posteror Ciliary Nerves
      - Loss of accommodation by patient
   4. Disruption major retinal vessel (rarely)
      - Vitreous hemorrhage

5. Retinal Vascular Occulsion (rarely)
   - Loss of vision

C. Excessive Energy

1. Puncture of Bruch's Membrane
   - Choroidal Neovascularization–Later
2. Vitreous contraction
   - Traction retinal detachment–Later
3. Choroidal rupture
   A. Choroidal Detachment
      1. serous
      2. hemorrhagic
   B. Vitreous Hemorrhage
4. Retinal Pigment Epithelial Rip
5. Retinal Hole (Rarely)
6. Angle Closure Glaucoma
   A. Ciliary body edema and forward rotation
   B. Anterior displacement of ciliary body by choroidal detachment
7. RPE hyperplasia and spread of scars

D. Exacerbation of pre-existing Diabetic Macular Edema–

Two treatment options to avoid this complication:

1. Treat diabetic macular edema in combination with inferior PRP (concomittantly) or
2. Treat diabetic macular edema in separate session prior ro commencing treatment of peripheral retina using panretinal photocoagulation.

2 MODIFIED GRID PHOTOCOAGULATION FOR DIABETIC MACULAR EDEMA

INDICATIONS, TECHNIQUES, AND COMPLICATIONS OF TREATMENT

INDICATION FOR MODIFIED GRID TREATMENT

Diffuse diabetic edema (with or without cystoid macular edema) is an indication for the modified grid treatment.

DEFINITION OF DIFFUSE DIABETIC MACULAR EDEMA

Diffuse diabetic macular edema is defined as the retinal thickening in the macula of two or more disc areas involving some portion of the foveal avascular zone (FAZ), with or without the presence of cystoid macular edema.

PRINCIPLES OF MODIFIED GRID TREATMENT

1. Primarily, grid treatment to areas of diffuse leakage (retinal thickening)
2. Concomitant treatment to areas of focal leakage located within or outside areas of diffuse edema
3. The modified grid treatment is <u>not</u> used to treat eyes requiring <u>focal treatment only</u>.

TECHNIQUE

Outpatient Procedure and Equipment

1. Topical anesthesia
2. Retrobulbar anesthesia may be needed for akinesia in patients who are likely to move.
   a. 2% lidocaine
   b. 150 units hyaluronidase (Wydase®)
3. Contact lenses
   a. Mainster posterior pole lens (This is the lens preferred by the authors.)
   b. Goldmann three mirror lens
   c. Yannuzzi laser lens

4. Recent fluorescein angiogram (within one month)
5. One frame projected behind patient
6. Laser surgeon refers constantly to IVFA
   a. To confirm macular landmarks during treatment
   b. To be certain treatment is applied to all areas of leakage seen in late frame IVFA and confirmed biomicroscopically (during treatment)

Overview–Modified Grid to Areas of Diffuse Edema

1. Argon green laser (514 nm)–preferred wavelength
2. 100 and 200 μ spots
3. Do not use 50 μ spots. These can perforate Bruch's membrane and cause choroidal neovascular membrane.
4. 0.1 second duration
5. 75 to 100 mw (Occasionally, higher power is needed.)
6. Light intensity burns

Modified Grid–Diffuse Edema Technique: Step 1

100 μ Spots–Juxtafoveal

1. Light intensity burns
2. Treat up to the edge of the foveal avascular zone (FAZ)
3. Place two to three rows of 100 μ spots in areas retinal thickening (clinically) or nonperfusion (on IVFA)
4. Space lesions one burn width apart

Treatment of Diffuse Diabetic Macular Edema with Modified Grid Laser Photocoagulation.

Step 1: 100 μ spots are placed up to the (FAZ) in areas of retinal thickening or nonperfusion.

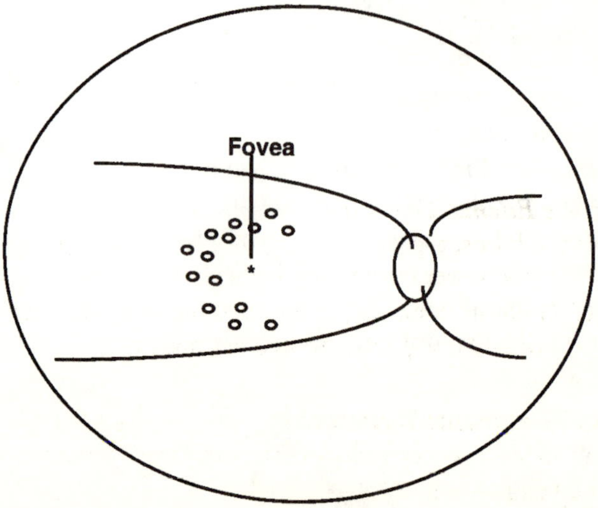

o=100 μ spots are placed up to the edge of FAZ in areas of retinal thickening or nonperfusion (on IVFA).

MODIFIED GRID–DIFFUSE EDEMA TECHNIQUE: STEP 2

150 to 200 μ spots–Outside the Area Treated with 100-μ Spots

1. Light intensity burns
2. Treat up to the edge of the area treated with 100-μ spots
3. Place 150 to 200 μ spots in all areas of retinal thickening (clinically) or nonperfusion (IVFA)
4. Space lesions one burn-width apart
5. Extend treatment peripherally to areas of uninvolved retina (no retinal thickening), determined by biomicroscopic examination or increased intensity of burn if placed in the normal retina

MODIFIED GRID INCLUDES CONCOMITANT TREATMENT OF AREAS OF DIFFUSE AND FOCAL LEAKAGE

Focal leakage is determined by:

1. biomicroscopic examination and
2. confirmed by IVFA

MODIFIED GRID FOCAL TREATMENT TECHNIQUE: DETAILED DESCRIPTION

1. Argon green (514 nm)–preferred wavelength
2. Areas focal leakage within or outside diffuse edema
3. 100 to 200 μ spots used
4. 0.1 second duration
5. Light to moderate intensity of burns
6. The preferred technique is somewhat lighter than ETDRS recommendation

SUMMARY

The four points below apply to both diffuse and focal treatment.

1. Argon green (514 nm)
2. 0.1 second duration
3. Light to moderate intensity of burns
4. 100 to 200 μ spots used

Diffuse Edema Treatment Techniques

1. 100 μ burns, typically, 50 to 100 burns placed juxtafoveally at 75 to 100 mw power (sometimes higher)
2. 200 μ burns, typically, 200 to 500 burns outside juxtafoveal burns at 100 to 200 mw power (sometimes higher)

Focal Treatment Techniques

Treat all areas as necessary in same treatment session.

1. 100 to 200 μ spots used
2. Light to moderate intensity of burns
3. Treat all areas focal leakage within or outside area of diffuse edema

TREATMENT OF DIFFUSE DIABETIC MACULAR EDEMA WITH MODIFIED GRID LASER PHOTOCOAGULATION.

Step 2: 200 μ spots are placed beyond 100 μ spots in areas of retinal thickening or nonperfusion.

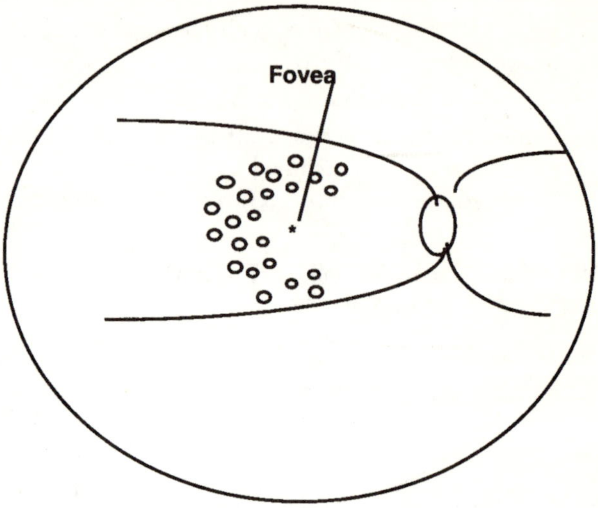

o=100 μ spots placed at edge of FAZ. **O**=200 μ spots placed at edge of 100 μ spots.

STEP 1

Place one to two rows of 100 micron burns in areas of retinal thickening or nonperfusion up to the edge of the Foveal Avascular Zone (FAZ). Burns should be of light intensity at the level of the Retinal Pigment Epithelium (RPE). Care should be taken to avoid the center of the fovea. If landmarks are obscure, stay well outside the FAZ with the treatment. Wait for some edema to resolve over the next three to four months. At the time of the retreatment, the landmarks may be easier to define.

TREATMENT OF DIFFUSE DIABETIC MACULAR EDEMA WITH MODIFIED GRID LASER PHOTOCOAGULATION.

Step 3: Focal treatment area. 100 to 200 μ spots are directed to focal areas of leakage confirmed on IVFA.

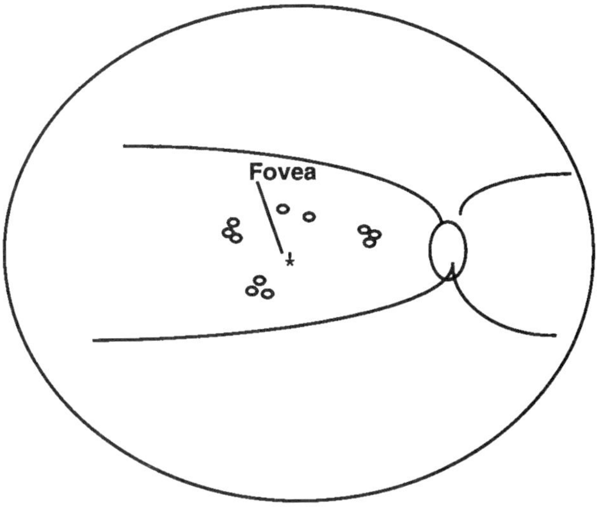

o=100 to 200 μ spots directed to areas of focal retinal thickening and late leakage (on IVFA).

STEP 2

Next, place 200 micron burns in areas of retinal thickening or nonperfusion in the area beyond the treatment with the 100 micron spots. Again, the burns should be of very light intensity at the level of the Retinal Pigment Epithelium (RPE). Wait for some edema to resolve over the next three to four months. If retreatment is necessary, landmarks may be better defined at that time.

STEP 3

Place 100 to 200 micron burns in areas with focal leakage within or outside the areas of diffuse edema. Burns should be of light intensity at the level of the Retinal Pigment Epithelium (REP)–not white-hot burns. Care should be taken to avoid the center of the fovea. If foveal landmarks are obscure, stay well outside the FAZ with the treatment. Wait for some of the edema to resolve over the next three to four months. At that time, if further treatment is indicated, the landmarks may be easier to visualize.

FOLLOW-UP

Both a focal and diffuse biomicroscopic and contact lens re-examination should take place at three to four months post-treatment to check for residual edema (CSME). If residual edema is present, repeat the IVFA and perform a supplemental laser treatment to the areas of retinal thickening (clincally detected) and/or non-perfusion (angiographically detected).

GUIDELINES AND TECHNIQUES FOR SUPPLEMENTAL TREATMENTS

Prior to the initial treatment, it is recommended that the practitioner advise the patient that supplemental treatment will likely be necessary. The patient, therefore, may require two to three treatments. Supplemental treatments are usually spaced at three to four month intervals over one year or more.

Description

1. Argon green (514 nm)
2. 100 to 200 μ spots
3. 0.1 second duration
4. Light to moderate intensity burns

Treat all areas of diffuse leakage seen on contact lens examination at slit lamp, and confirmed on IVFA. The practitioner may place the grid throughout the areas of retinal thickening or nonperfusion that were previously treated if edema persists in that area. It is likely that the previous burns may be invisible. Evaluate the patient every three to four months for further treatment. Supplemental treatment may be reapplied according to the guidelines given.

COMPLICATIONS

1. Improper focus
   a. Inadvertent foveal photocoagulation
   b. Cataract (improper focus into lens)
   c. Cornea burns (improper focus on cornea)
2. Excessive energy
   a. Spreading of laser lesion scars into fovea during treatment
   b. Nerve fiber layer defects (burns spread upward into NFL)
   c. Choroidal rupture (break in Bruch's membrane)
      i. Hemorrhage (may damage overlying retina)
      ii. Later, choroidal neovascularization
   d. Retinal hole (rare)
3. Side effects
   a. Temporary blurring of vision (resolves in one to two weeks in most cases)
   b. Temporary scotomas corresponding to treated areas (resolves over a few months in most cases)

3 Laser Treatment of Venous Occlusive Disease of the Retinal Vessels

Indications, Techniques, and Complications of Treatment

Laser treatment may be required for ischemic or non-ischemic Central Retinal Vein Occlusion (CRVO). Ischemic CRVO may require either panretinal photocoagulation (PRP) or macular edema treatment or both. Nonischemic CRVO may require macular edema treatment.

Both Branch and Hemiretinal Vein Occlusions may be ischemic and require retinal photocoagulation. A quadrantic PRP is performed for an ischemic Branch Retinal Vein Occlusion (BRVO) and a hemiretinal PRP is performed for an ischemic Hemiretinal Vein Occlusion(HRVO).

Indications

Indications for panretinal photocoagulation in venous occlusive disease include proliferative disease manifested by retinal neovascularization, rubeosis, or vitreous hemorrhage and large areas of retinal non-perfusion on IVFA. Generally, ten disc areas of retinal non-perfusion on IVFA in a CRVO and five disc areas of retinal non-perfusion on IVFA in a BRVO are relative indications for PRP.

Techniques

Single-session PRP can be performed to treat any of the three types of Retinal Venous Occulsions when treatment is indicated. Because of the large number of burns required, however, CRVO treatment in multiple sessions is recommended. The number of laser burns suggested is determined by the number of sessions in which treatment is applied and the type of neovascularization present. The recommendations below are guidelines and treatment should be individualized for each patient.

Single Session PRP	*Number of Burns/Session*
BRVO	600-800
HRVO	800-1200
CRVO (sometimes)	1200-2000

Multiple Session PRP	*Neovascularization Elsewhere*	*Neovascularization of Disc*
HRVO	600-1000 NVE	800-1200 NVD
CRVO (usually)	800-1200 NVE	1400-1600 NVD

Anesthesia

1. Topical (prior to retrobulbar)
2. Retrobulbar (preferable in most patients)
   a. Recommended retrobulbar 50:50 mixture: 0.75% Marcaine, 2.0% Xylocaine, and 150 IU Hyaluronidase (Wydase®)
3. Peribulbar (if monocular)
4. General (rare)
   a. Use Laser Indirect Ophthalmoscope (LIO) in this case (See Tape 5)

Contact Lenses to Use at Slit Lamp (lowest magnification)

1. Rodenstock panfunduscopic lens (preferred)
2. Quadraspheric (Volk) lens
3. Mainster Wide Field lens
4. 3-Mirror Goldmann lens (It is possible to lose sight of the fovea and inadvertently treat it)

Argon Green Laser Treatment

1. Wavelength (514 nm)
2. Parameters
   a. 200 to 500 micron spot size
   b. 0.1 seconds duration (The practitioner may use 0.05 seconds in very pain-sensitive patients.)
   c. 300 to 750 mw average power settings

Dye, Krypton Red, and Diode Laser Treatments

1. Wavelengths
   a. Dye (630 or 640 nm)
   b. Krypton Red (647 nm)
   c. Diode (810 nm)
   d. Notes: Longer wavelengths are useful for treating eyes with cataracts, vitreous hemorrhages, and other media opacities, however, longer wavelengths may rupture Bruch's membrane more readily. Use longer duration and lower power settings to avoid this.
2. Parameters
   a. 200 to 500 micron spot size
   b. 0.2 seconds duration (Note longer time with these wavelengths.)
   c. 300 to 750 mw average

TECHNIQUE FOR PANRETINAL PHOTOCOAGULATION FOR PROLIFERATIVE CRVO AND HRVO.

Step 1: Placement barrier rows temporal to fovea.

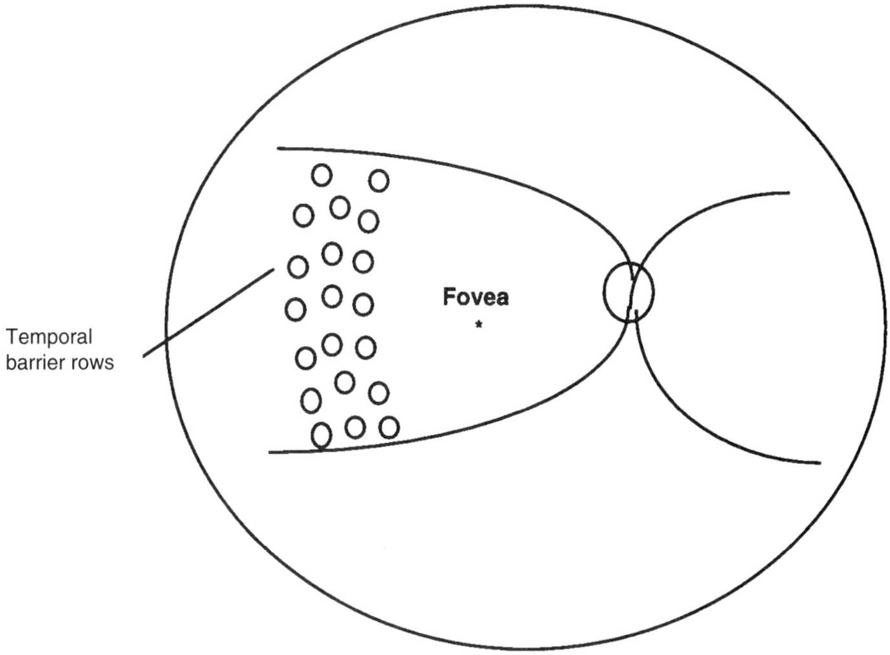

O=500 μ burns placed with Rodenstock Lens are 700 to 750 μ at retina.

PRP TECHNIQUES

Treatment is initiated with the placement of two to three rows of burns in an arcuate pattern placed two to three disc diameters temporal to the fovea. This provides a barrier landmark and keeps the laser surgeon from inadvertently treating the fovea. Laser power is titrated during the barrier row placement to achieve a moderately intense white burn. Spots are placed one burn width apart.

Place two to three barrier rows to ensure the visibility of the temporal edge of the macular area. These laser spots are very crucial landmarks to assure safe treatment. Take the time to ensure that both you and the patient are seated at the slit lamp comfortably without straining. Also, take the time to get the posterior pole into sharp focus at the beginning of the treatment.

Technique for Panretinal Photocoagulation for Proliferative Retinal Venous Occlusive Disease.

Step 2: Beginning treatment peripheral retina.

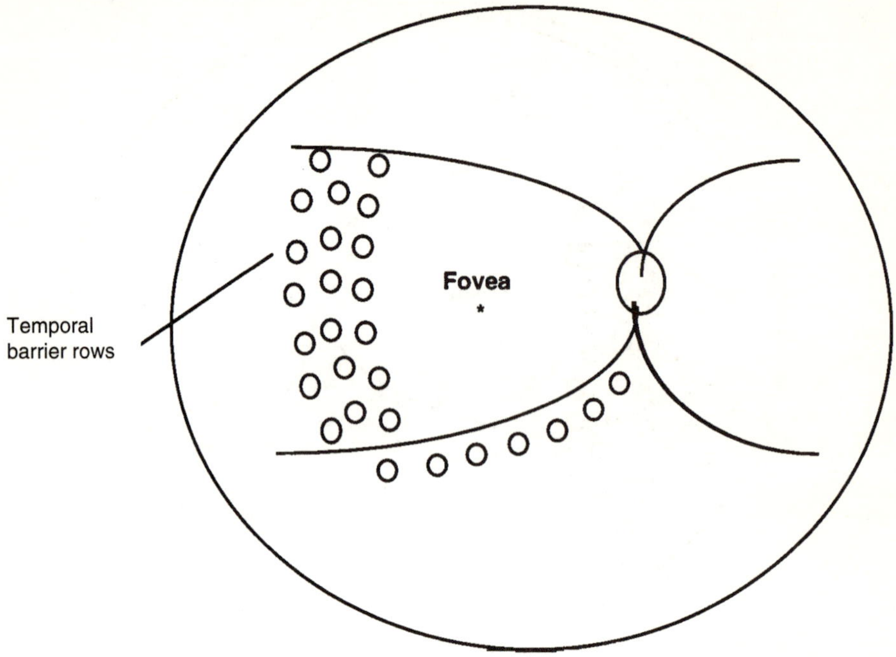

O=500 μ burns placed with Rodenstock Lens are 700 to 750 μ at retina.

CRVO or HRVO Techniques

Following placement of the temporal barrier rows, begin treating each quadrant starting one-half to one disc diameter from the optic disc and moving outward along the major retinal vessels toward the periphery. Space the burns one-half to one burn width from the vessel walls and leave one burn width between burns. Always know the location of the fovea in relation to where you are treating. If you are not certain, stop and locate the fovea prior to proceeding.

Care should be taken to avoid the major vessels. If a retinal vessel is inadvertently treated, usually only a vasospasm will result, not a rupture. It is unusual to cause a complete vascular occlusion during this treatment, but always try to avoid major vessels to eliminate the possibility of a vascular occlusion.

TECHNIQUE FOR PANRETINAL PHOTOCOAGULATION FOR PROLIFERATIVE RETINAL VENOUS OCCLUSIVE DISEASE.

Step 3: Treatment of inferior peripheral retina.

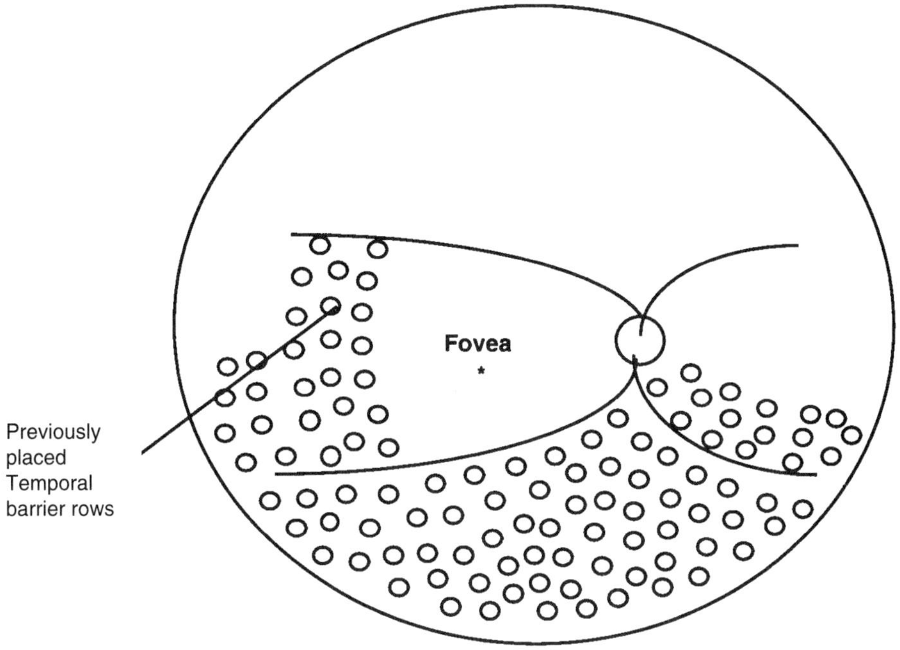

Complete treatment of inferior peripheral retina placing burns outward along inferior major vessels toward periphery. Space burns one-burn width apart and fill in areas between major vessels as shown in diagram.

CRVO OR INFERIOR HRVO TECHNIQUE

In CRVO, treat the inferior retina first, if possible, in case the neovascularization bleeds before the second session. Place the burns along the inferior major retinal vessels and space the burns one-half to one burn width from the vessel walls. Starting near the disc and moving out to the periphery, leave one burn width between burns as you fill in the areas between the inferior major retinal vessels. Tilt the lens in the far periphery to focus on one area of the peripheral retina. Adjust the slit lamp as well, to get one crescent-shaped area of the retina in focus at one time. Then, treat all areas of the retina that are in focus and reposition the contact lens to view another contiguous area of the peripheral retina. It will be necessary to readjust the slit lamp to get this next area of peripheral retina into focus. Fill in one quadrant at a time in a systematic manner to insure that there are no areas of the peripheral retina inferiorly that are left untreated.

TECHNIQUE FOR PANRETINAL PHOTOCOAGULATION FOR PROLIFERATIVE RETINAL VENOUS OCCLUSIVE DISEASE.

Step 4: Treatment of superior peripheral retina.

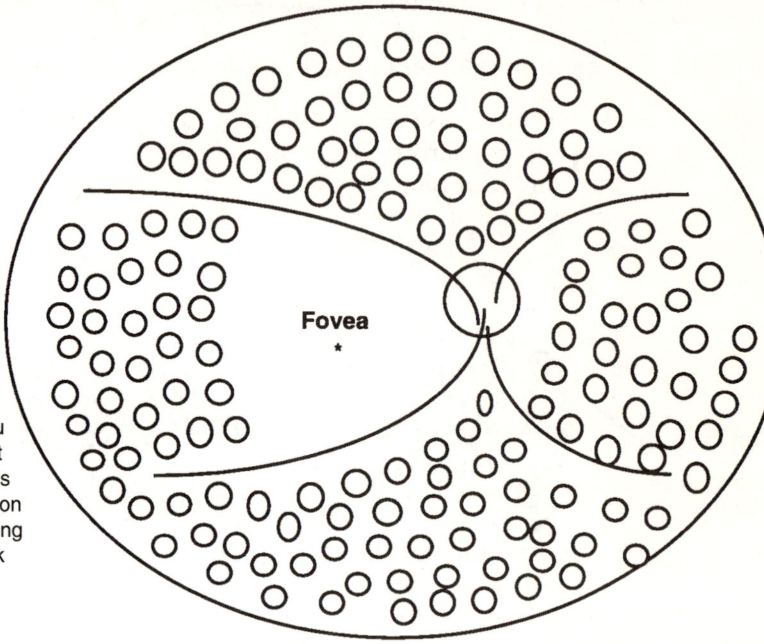

O Again use 500µ spot size on slit lamp. This gives 700-750µ spot on retina when using the Rodenstock lens.

Fill in burns in the superior retina in the manner described for the inferior retina. Start near the disc and place burns along major superior vessels. Place burns one-burn width apart. Tilt lens to clearly view the peripheral retina. Note that you may have to decrease the power in the periphery because the retina is thinner in this location. O Use 500 µ spot size on slit lamp. This gives 700 to 750 µ spot on retina when using the Rodenstock lens.

PERIPHERAL SUPERIOR RETINAL TREATMENT TECHNIQUES

As the retina thins in the periphery, the laser power needed to achieve the correct burn intensity may decrease. Tilt the lens in the far periphery to focus on the area of the peripheral retina as described previously. Adjust the slit lamp, as well, to get one crescent-shaped area in focus at a time and adjust the power to achieve a grey-white burn. Then all the areas of the peripheral retina that are in focus can be completely treated. To treat another area of the peripheral retina, the slit lamp and the contact lens must both be readjusted and refocused. Do one quadrant at a time, beginning near the superior disc and moving out to periphery. Tilt the contact lens in the far periphery as described. Consider treatment for patients following the guidelines for CRVO, BRVO, or hemi (HRVO).

POSTOPERATIVE CARE AFTER PRP

If a retrobulbar anesthetic is given, instill an antibiotic/steroid ointment into the treated eye and cover it with a patch for four to six hours, until the lid moves. Start topical steroids when the patch is removed (but not if the patient is a steroid reponder, historically.) The topical steroids should be administered three to four times daily for five to seven days.

A postoperative visit should take place in seven to ten days. Perform gonioscopy regularly to detect rubeosis. See patient every two to four weeks until regression of proliferative disease occurs. Do a fill-in PRP or transconjunctival anterior retinal cryopexy for nonregressing neovascularization (See Tape 6).

Key Points

Place barrier rows every time (for CRVO and HRVO). Note where the fovea is at all times during the treatment. Do not treat directly over areas with elevated neovascularization, as this may cause vitreous contraction. Avoid treatment over major retinal vessels. Keep the slit lamp on the lowest magnification for the best view of the peripheral retina.

COMPLICATIONS OF PRP FOR VENOUS OCCLUSIVE DISEASE

A. Poor overview of Retinal Topography or Poor visualization of Landmarks
Foveal photocoagulation

B. Incorrect Focus
1. Corneal Burns
2. Lenticular Burns
3. Treatment over Long Posteror Ciliary Nerves
    - Loss of accommodation by patient
4. Disruption major retinal vessel (rarely)
    - Vitreous hemorrhage
5. Retinal Vascular Occulsion (rarely)
- Loss of vision

C. Excessive Energy
1. Puncture of Bruch's Membrane
    - Choroidal Neovascularization–Later
2. Vitreous contraction
    - Traction retinal detachment–Later
3. Choroidal rupture
    A. Choroidal Detachment
        1. serous
        2. hemorrhagic
    B. Vitreous Hemorrhage
4. Retinal Pigment Epithelial Rip
5. Retinal Hole (Rarely)
6. Angle Closure Glaucoma
    A. Ciliary body edema and forward rotation
    B. Anterior displacement of ciliary body by choroidal detachment

MACULAR EDEMA SECONDARY TO RETINAL VENOUS OCCLUSIVE DISEASE

Macular edema is found in both ischemic vein occlusions and nonischemic vein occlusions and in all types of venous occlusions, namely CRVO, HRVO, and BRVO.

INDICATIONS FOR MACULAR GRID TREATMENT IN VENOUS OCCLUSIVE DISEASE

1. Vision <20/40 at three months following the event
2. Retinal thickening in macula
3. Although not an indication, areas of retinal non-perfusion (angiographically) should be treated at the same time indicated treatment is applied.

CONTACT LENSES TO USE AT SLIT LAMP (MEDIUM MAGNIFICATION)

1. Mainster posterior pole lens (preferred)
2. Yannuzzi posterior pole laser lens
3. 3-Mirror Goldmann lens
4. Goldmann fundus lens (flat)

TREATMENT OF MACULAR EDEMA DUE TO CENTRAL RETINAL OR HEMIRETINAL VEIN OCCLUSION.

Step 1: 100 µ spots are placed surrounding and up to the FAZ in areas of retinal thickening or nonperfusion (from IVFA).

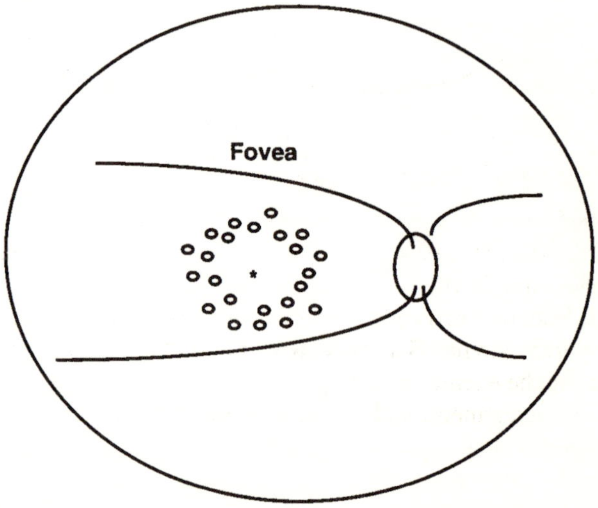

o=100 µ spots placed up to the edge of FAZ in areas of retinal thickening or nonperfusion (on IVFA).

MACULAR EDEMA TECHNIQUE

Place one to two rows of 100 micron burns in areas of retinal thickening or nonperfusion up to the edge of the Foveal Avascular Zone (FAZ). Burns should be of light intensity at the level of the retinal pigment epithelium (RPE). Care should be taken to avoid the center of the fovea- if the landmarks are obscure, stay further outside the edge of the FAZ with treatment. Wait for edema to resolve over the next three to four months. At the time of retreatment, the landmarks may be better defined.

TREATMENT OF MACULAR EDEMA DUE TO CENTRAL RETINAL OR HEMIRETINAL VEIN OCCLUSION.

Step 2: 150 to 200 μ spots in areas of retinal thickening or nonperfusion.

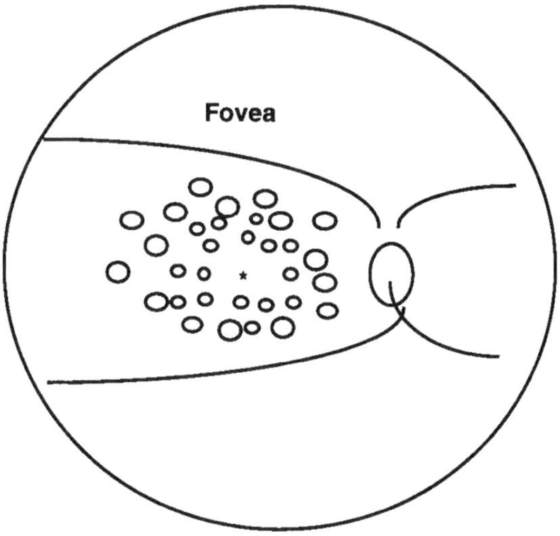

o=100 μ spots placed at edge of FAZ.
O 150 to 200 μ spots placed outside edge of 100 μ spots.

Next, place 150 to 200 micron burns in the areas of retinal thickening or nonperfusion in the area outside the treatment with the 100 micron spots, spacing burns one burn-width apart. Again, the burns should be of a very light intensity at the level of the retinal pigment epithelium (RPE). Wait for the edema to resolve over the next three to four months. At the time of retreatment, landmarks may be better defined.

Treatment of Macular Edema Due to Branch Retinal Vein Occlusion.

Step 1: 100 µ spots are placed surrounding and up to the edge of the FAZ in areas of retinal thickening or nonperfusion secondary to the vein occlusion.

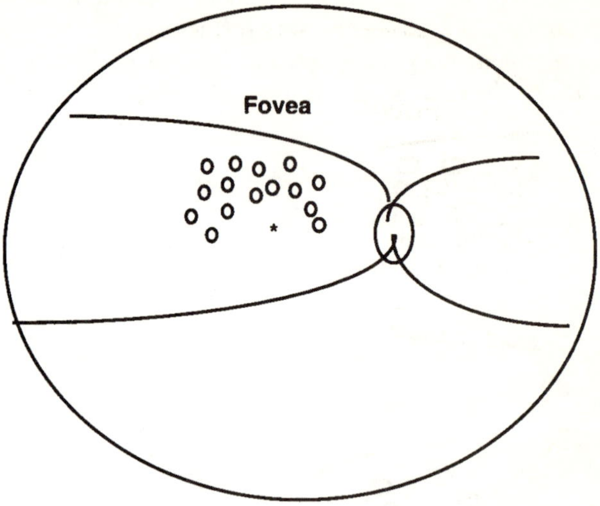

o=100 µ spots placed up to edge of the FAZ in areas of retinal thickening or nonperfusion.

Place one to two rows of 100 micron burns in the areas of retinal thickening or nonperfusion up to the edge of the foveal avascular zone (FAZ) in the areas affected by BRVO. The burns should be of a light intensity at the level of the retinal pigment epithelium (RPE). Care should be taken to avoid the center of the fovea - if landmarks are obscure, stay further outside the edge of the FAZ with treatment. Wait for the edema to resolve over the next three to four months. If retreatment is necessary at that time, the landmarks may be better defined.

TREATMENT OF MACULAR EDEMA DUE TO BRANCH RETINAL VEIN OCCLUSION.

Step 2: 150 to 200 μ spots are placed in areas of retinal thickening or nonperfusion secondary to the branch or hemiretinal vein occlusion that surround the areas treated with 100 μ spots.

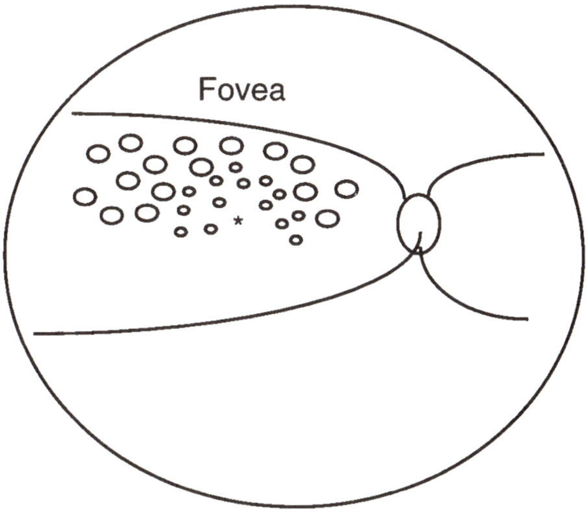

o=100 μ spots in areas of macular edema.
O=200 μ spots in areas of macular edema.

Place 150 to 200 micron burns in the areas of retinal thickening or nonperfusion outside the 100-micron burns <u>in the areas affected by the BRVO</u>. The burns should be of a light intensity at the level of the retinal pigment epithelium (RPE). Wait for the edema to resolve over the next three to four months. At the time of retreatment, landmarks may be better defined.

COMPLICATIONS OF MACULAR EDEMA TREATMENT IN VENOUS OCCLUSIVE DISEASE

1. Improper Focus may allow
   a. Photocoagulation of the fovea
   b. Cataract (improper focus into lens)
   c. Corneal Burn (improper focus into cornea)
2. Excessive energy may result in
   a. Spreading of laser scars into fovea
   b. Nerve fiber layer defects
   c. Choroidal rupture (with hemorrhage and later subretinal neovascularization)
   d. Retinal hole (rare)
3. Side effects of treatment–Temporary Scotomas
   a. Corresponding to areas of treatment
   b. Usually resolve over time

4 Laser Treatment of Subretinal (Choroidal) Neovascularization

Indications, Techniques, and Complications of Treatment

The classification of choroidal neovascular membranes is based on their location relative to the center of the fovea.

Location	Distance from Center of Fovea
Extrafoveal	200 to 2500 microns
Juxtafoveal	1 to 199 microns
Subfoveal	0 (Beneath center of Fovea)

Following laser treatment, if a residual choroidal neovascular membrane is present, it is classified based on its time of appearance after treatment. A choroidal neovascular membrane demonstrated on IVFA by dye leakage at the periphery of the photocoagulation scar within six weeks of laser treatment is considered persistent. A choroidal neovascular membrane demonstrated on IVFA by dye leakage at the periphery of the photocoagulation scar more than six weeks after laser treatment is considered recurrent.

Macular Photocoagulation Study (MPS) recommendations are only applied to well defined choroidal neovascular lesions. No recommendations have been given for treatment of ill defined choroidal neovascular lesions (diffuse ooze).

Treatment Techniques

Anesthesia

1. Topical anesthesia
2. Retrobulbar anesthesia (This may be needed for akinesia in patients who are likely to move.)
   a. 2% lidocaine
   b. 150 units hyaluronidase (Wydase®)

Contact Lenses

1. Mainster posterior pole lens (preferred)
2. Goldmann three mirror lens
3. Yannuzzi laser lens

Fluorescein Angiogram
Treatment of all choroidal neovascular membranes requires a recent fluorescein angiogram (within 96 hours). One frame must be projected behind the patient. The laser surgeon must refer constantly to the IVFA to confirm the macular landmarks during treatment, and to be certain the treatment is applied to all the areas of leakage seen in the late IVFA frames and confirmed biomicroscopically (during the treatment).

Extrafoveal Membranes
The goal of extrafoveal choroidal neovascular membrane treatment is a moderately intense white burn covering the entire neovascular complex. An argon green laser (514 nm) is preferred.

The first step in treatment is to outline the lesion. Use IVFA to get 100 µ beyond the edge of the lesion on all sides, utilizing 100 µ spots of 0.1 sec duration. Burns must be of very light intensity. Space lesions one burn-width apart. Outline the entire lesion.

TREATMENT OF EXTRAFOVEAL CHOROIDAL NEOVASCULAR MEMBRANE. OUTLINING THE LESION.

Step 1: Treatment begins by outlining lesion with 100 µ Argon Green Spots of very light intensity.

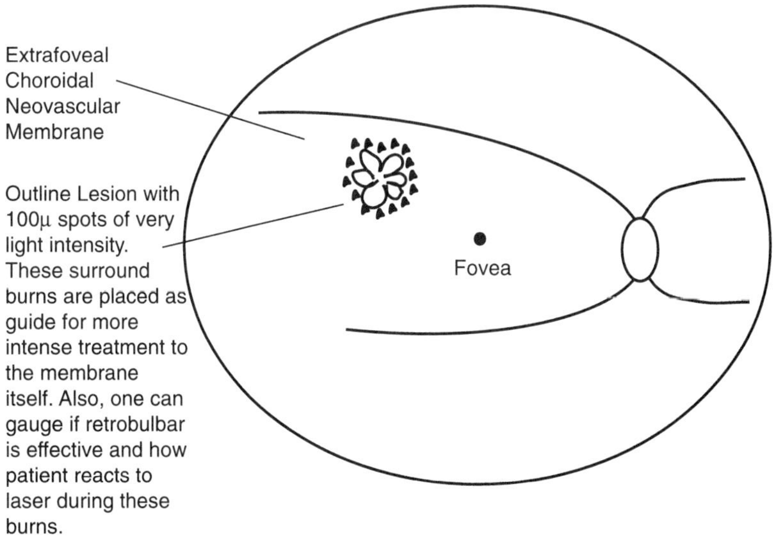

Photocoagulation begins on the foveal side of the membrane to avoid the occasional complication wherein bleeding from the neovascularization is induced on the opposite side of the membrane when treatment begins, causing it to spread under the fovea if treatment is initiated on the nonfoveal side and this may compromise the final visual acuity. If using krypton red or dye laser, do not outline lesion, as these wavelengths at 100 µ may perforate Bruch's membrane.

The next step is treatment on the foveal side of the lesion which requires 100 to 200 μ confluent spots on the foveal side of the lesion 0.2 to 0.5 seconds duration. Burns must be of moderately heavy intensity. Extend treatment 100 μ beyond the edge of the lesion. Place lesions confluently.

TREATMENT OF EXTRAFOVEAL CHOROIDAL NEOVASCULAR MEMBRANE. TREATMENT OF FOVEAL SIDE OF LESION.

Step 2: Treat foveal side of lesion with confluent burns 200 to 500 μ placed at moderately white intensity.

Confluently placed 200-500μ spots on foveal side of lesion. Place pilot burn at non-foveal edge of membrane to judge power intensity.

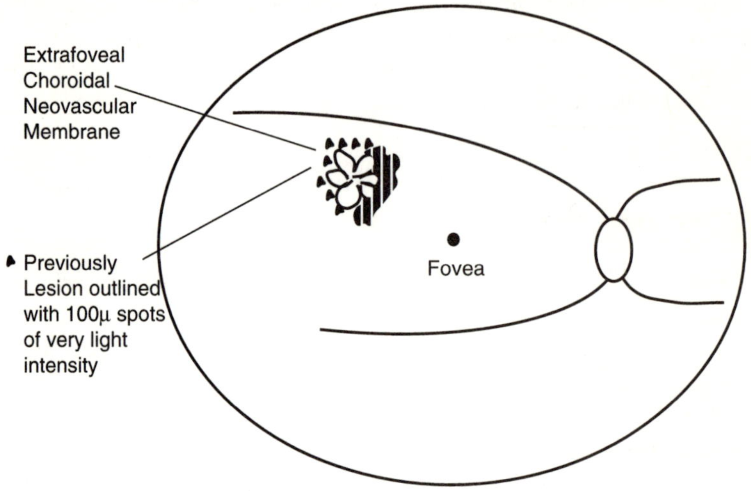

Surgeon should increase laser power to produce a moderately intense whitening of membrane. Retreatment over moderately intense burns is typically less effective than to achieve whitening during initial treatment.

The last step is the treatment of the remainder of extrafoveal lesions which requires 200 to 500 μ spots over the remainder of the entire lesion, of 0.5 to 1.0 seconds duration. Burns must be of chalk-white intensity. Extend treatment 100 μ beyond the edge of the lesion. Place the lesions confluently and overlapping.

TREATMENT OF REMAINDER OF ENTIRE EXTRAFOVEAL LESION.

Step 3: Overlapping 200 to 500 μ burns are placed confluently to cover entire lesion. These should be of chalk-white intensity.

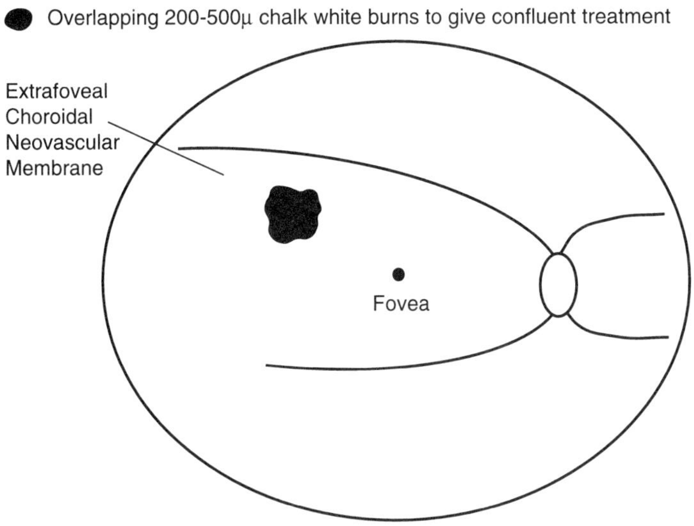

Previously, lesion was outlined with 100 μ spots of very light intensity and foveal side of lesion was treated with 200 to 500 μ burns of moderate intensity. After concluding confluent laser treatment, the laser surgeon should check the extent of the treatment against angiogram to be absolutely certain that the entire membrane and zone of blocked fluorescence has been treated with intense photocoagulation.

SUMMARY OF TREATMENT OF EXTRAFOVEAL CHOROIDAL NEOVASCULAR MEMBRANES

1. Argon Green laser preferred
2. Outline lesion with 100 μ spots of very light intensity
3. Treat foveal side of lesion with 100 to 200 μ spots of moderately heavy intensity
4. Treat remainder of lesion in a confluent menner with 200 to 500 μ chalk white burns in an overlapping manner.

Juxtafoveal Membranes

The goal of juxtafoveal choroidal neovascular membrane treatment is a moderately intense white burn covering the entire neovascular complex - Avoid the central foveal if possible.

Wavelengths

1. Krypton red laser (647 nm) (preferred)
2. Argon green laser (514 nm) (Absorption by Xanthophyll pigment in fovea is possible.)
3. Dye laser (630 to 640 nm)

TECHNIQUE

1. Begin with low power settings (100 to 200 mw)
2. Increase in 25 mw increments
3. Do not outline the lesion first with krypton red or dye laser (only if using the argon green wavelength)

TREATMENT OF JUXTAFOVEAL CHOROIDAL NEOVASCULAR MEMBRANE.

Step 1: Outline of juxtafoveal lesion first only when treating with argon green wavelength.

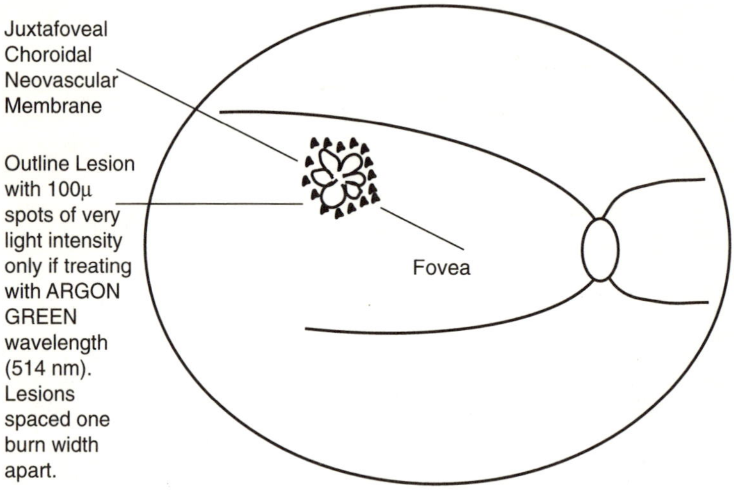

Do not outline lesion if using krypton red (647 nm) or dye laser (638-640 nm) because it is possible to perforate Bruch's membrane with 100 µ burns when outlining lesion using these wavelengths.

Specific treatment points using either krypton red (647 nm) or a dye laser (630 to 640 nm) are to start at low power (100 to 200 mw) and increase in 25-mw increments. Remember: Do not outline the lesion (as described previously) with these wavelength lasers. Only use the outlining technique with the argon green wavelength.

The next treatment step of the juxtafoveal membrane using argon green or krypton red or a dye laser is to begin on the foveal side of the membrane after the pilot burns are titrated on the nonfoveal side of the lesion. 200 to 500 µ overlapping spots are placed to create a confluent burn. Moderately intense burns should be the goal. When possible, it is recommended to treat 100 µ beyond the edge of the membrane. If the neovascular complex extends into the FAZ, it is recommended that the surgeon treat up to edge of the fovea and try to avoid treating the fovea. If the choroidal neovascular membrane is subfoveal, the surgeon should use the guidelines recommended by the MPS study. (See next page). Remember: Do not outline the lesion with krypton red or a dye laser.

TREATMENT OF JUXTAFOVEAL CHOROIDAL NEOVASCULAR MEMBRANE.

Step 2: Treat all juxtafoveal lesions on the foveal side using overlapping 200 to 500 μ burns of moderate intensity to create a confluent burn at this location.

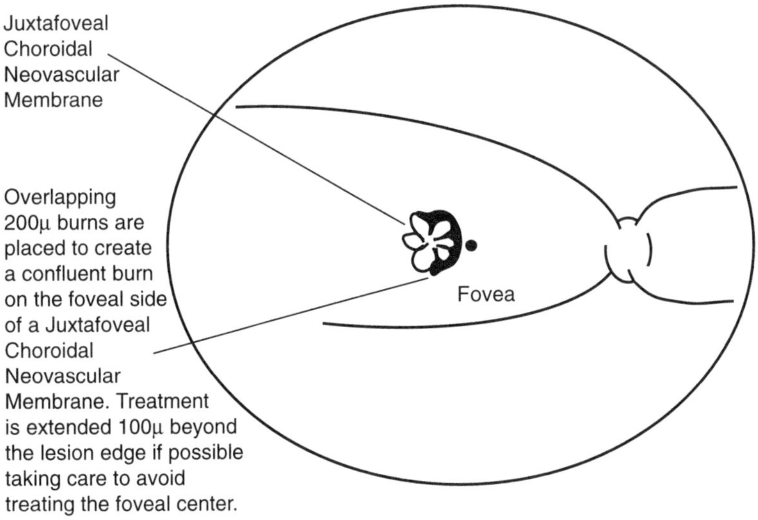

CNV whose foveal edge is at or within the margin of the FAZ cannot be delimited with outlining burns in that area. Such membranes should be treated with overlapping burns of argon green (514 nm), krypton red (647 nm), or dye laser (630-640 nm) with 200 to 500 μ spot size at 0.2 to 0.5 seconds duration. When using krypton red, it is advisable to use 500 μ spots for 0.5 seconds.

After treating the foveal side of the juxtafoveal lesion, the last step is to treat the remainder of the lesion confluently, using 200 to 500 μ overlapping burns of 0.5 to 1.0-second duration. The end point is uniform intense chalk-white burns that cover the entire lesion confluently. (Note: see diagram, page 34). Check the extent of treatment against IVFA to insure that the entire membrane and zone of blocked fluorescence is treated.

SUMMARY OF TREATMENT OF JUXTAFOVEAL CHOROIDAL NEOVASCULAR MEMBRANES

1. Krypton Red or Dye laser preferred
2. DO NOT outline lesion with 100 μ spots (unless using argon green)
3. Treat foveal side of lesion with 200 to 500 μ spots of moderately heavy intensity
4. Treat remainder of lesion in a confluent manner with 200 to 500 μ chalk white burns in an overlapping manner

MPS GUIDELINES USED FOR TREATING A <u>NEW</u> SUBFOVEAL MEMBRANE

1. A newly documented lesion located beneath the foveal center

2. Well-defined "classical" choroidal neovascular membrane on IVFA
3. Size not greater than 3.5 disc areas
4. Best corrected visual acuity not better than 20/40 and not worse than 20/320
5. Age not less than 50 years

MPS GUIDELINES USED FOR TREATING A RECURRENT SUBFOVEAL MEMBRANE

1. Extension into the foveal center of a previously treated juxtafoveal or extrafoveal membrane
2. Well-defined "classical" choroidal neovascular membrane on IVFA
3. Size of recurrent membrane and prior laser scar not greater than 6 disc areas with some uninvolved retina within 1500 μ of the foveal center
4. Best corrected visual acuity not better than 20/40 and not worse than 20/320
5. Age not less than 50 years

TREATMENT TECHNIQUE–NEW SUBFOVEAL CHOROIDAL NEOVASCULAR MEMBRANE (CNV)

1. Treat all CNV and extend 100 μ beyond all components except blood
2. Treat boundaries of lesion with:
   200 to 500 μ spot size
   0.2 to 0.5 seconds
3. Treat within boundaries of lesions confluently with:
   200 to 500 μ spot size
   0.5 to 1.0 seconds

TREATMENT TECHNIQUE–RECURRENT SUBFOVEAL CHOROIDAL NEOVASCULAR MEMBRANE (CNV)

1. Treat all CNV and extend 100 μ beyond all components except blood
2. Extend treatment 300 μ into previous laser scar at interface with Recurrent lesion
3. Treat feeder vessels 100 μ beyond their lateral border and 300 μ radially beyond feeder vessel origin
4. Treat boundaries with:
   200 to 500 μ spot size
   0.2 to 0.5 seconds
3. Treat within boundaries of lesions confluently with:
   200 to 500 μ spot size
   0.5 to 1.0 seconds

TREATMENT OF NEW AND RECURRENT SUBFOVEAL CHOROIDAL NEOVASCULAR MEMBRANES.

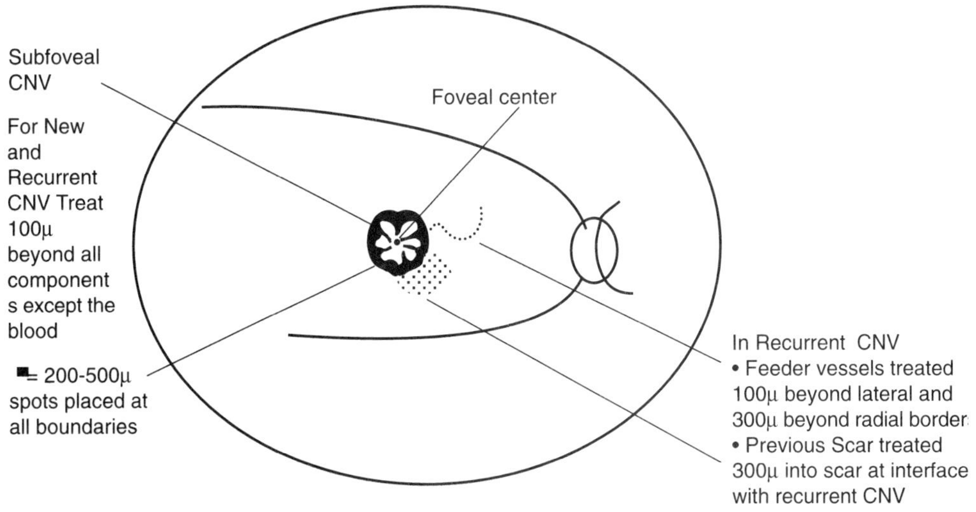

For both new and recurrent CNV, after confluently treating all boundaries with 200 to 500 µ spots, the entire lesion should be treated confluently with 200 to 500 µ spots at a longer duration to cover the entire lesion with laser treatment.

SUMMARY OF TREATMENT OF SUBFOVEAL CHOROIDAL NEOVASCULAR MEMBRANES

1. Treat 100 µ beyond all components except blood
2. Boundaries are treated with 200 to 500 µ spots of moderately heavy intensity
3. Treat remainder of lesion in a confluent manner with 200 to 500 µ chalk white burns in an overlapping manner

RECOMMENDED CHOICE OF WAVELENGTH FOR PERSISTENT OR RECURRENT CNV

Extrafoveal
Argon pure green (514nm)
Juxtafoveal or Subfoveal
Krypton red 647 nm
Dye laser 630 nm
Argon pure green (514nm)

When re-treating Persistent or Recurrent choroidal neovascularization (Extrafoveal, Juxtafoveal or Subfoveal), it is recommended to use the same laser modality and treatment parameters used in the treatment of the primary CNV.

Followup

Following laser treatment, a clinical examination and IVFA at one to two weeks, four to six weeks, two to three months, and six months are recommended. Treatment should be reapplied as deemed necessary at these examinations. The patient should use the Amsler grid if possible between visits as well as throughout the continuous followup period.

Complications

Complications include unintentional foveal treatment (during treatment for extrafoveal/juxtafoveal membranes–poor focus), wrinkling of internal limiting membrane (excessive energy), perforation of Bruch's membrane (small spot size, excessive energy), hemorrhage from the CNM (stopped by directly treating over hemorrhage), retinal pigment epithelial (RPE) rip (excessive energy), lenticular or corneal burns (poor focus), or a retinal hole (rare, excessive energy).

5 Laser Indirect Ophthalmoscopic Treatment of Retinal Disease

Indications, Techniques, and Complications of Treatment

Indications

Indications for the use of the Laser Indirect Ophthalmoscope (LIO) are to perform supplemental panretinal photocoagulation to anterior retina in eyes with ischemic and proliferative retinopathy due to diabetes, an ischemic central retinal vein occlusion, carotid occlusive disease, intermediate uveitis, or other causes. In addition, initial or supplemental PRP can be performed in children and uncooperative adults who need general anesthesia, patients unable to position comfortably at slit lamp because of body size or shape (scoliosis, large chest size), or head tremor. Occasionally, postoperative patients with drowsiness secondary to residual effects of general anesthesia cannot sit at a slit lamp and can be treated with the LIO. Anterior peripheral retinal pathology may be visualized easier with LIO, including such lesions as retinal tears or holes that need treatment, peripheral retinal tumors (small melanoma, angioma), retinopathy of prematurity (stage III), treatment on existing retinal buckles or sponges, or retinal dialysis (idiopathic or traumatic). Often, intraoperative and postoperative pathology requires LIO, specifically (a) peripheral retinal pathology where treatment with curved endolaser probe is dangerous to use, (b) limited visibility of retinal pathology in the eyes with vitreous substitutes, air- or gas-filled eyes, silicone- or perfluorocarbon-filled eyes, vitreous hemorrhage dispersed in vitreous cavity, corneal edema, or cataract, (c) limited visibility due to anterior segment distortion, specifically post-traumatic corneal irregularities or sutures or postoperative corneal sutures, striae, edema, or scars. In the postoperative period contact lens placement for laser treatment at slit lamp may be difficult and the view-impaired because of ocular tenderness, a trabeculectomy bleb of large size, a shallow anterior chamber, corneal striae or corneal scars limiting a clear view of the retina. Any lenticular or vitreous opacity may also obstruct a clear view of the retina. The LIO may afford a view without placing a contact lens on the eye thus affording a mechanism to treat these difficult eyes.

Anesthesia

1. Topical (prior to retrobulbar)
2. Peribulbar (if monocular)

3. Retrobulbar
   Use a 50:50 mixture:
   0.75% Marcaine, 2.0% Xylocaine, 150 IU hyaluronidase (Wydase®)
4. General (LIO is useful during surgical procedures when the patient is asleep)

Safety features for personnel and patients include a safety filter for the surgon (built into the LIO), safety goggles for assistants and observers, and a patch for the opposite eye of the patient (contralateral from the treated eye.)

14, 20, and 28 diopter condensing lenses are needed. Other needed supplies are: lid speculum, balanced salt solution, topical anesthetic, and scleral depressor.

Determinants of LIO spot size on the retina are dependent on the variable optics to change in spot size on LIO (some models) and fixed spot size in LIO (some models). The laser beam spot size at the retina depends on the distance of the surgeon from the patient, the power of the condensing lens used by the surgeon, and the refractive status of the patient's eye.

LIO SPOT SIZE RETINA. REMOVABLE FOCUSING LENSES FOR SURGEONS WITH LONGER ARMS ALTER THE LOCATION OF THE FOCAL POINT IN SPACE BUT DO NOT CHANGE THE DIAMETER (SIZE) OF BEAM AT THE FOCAL POINT.

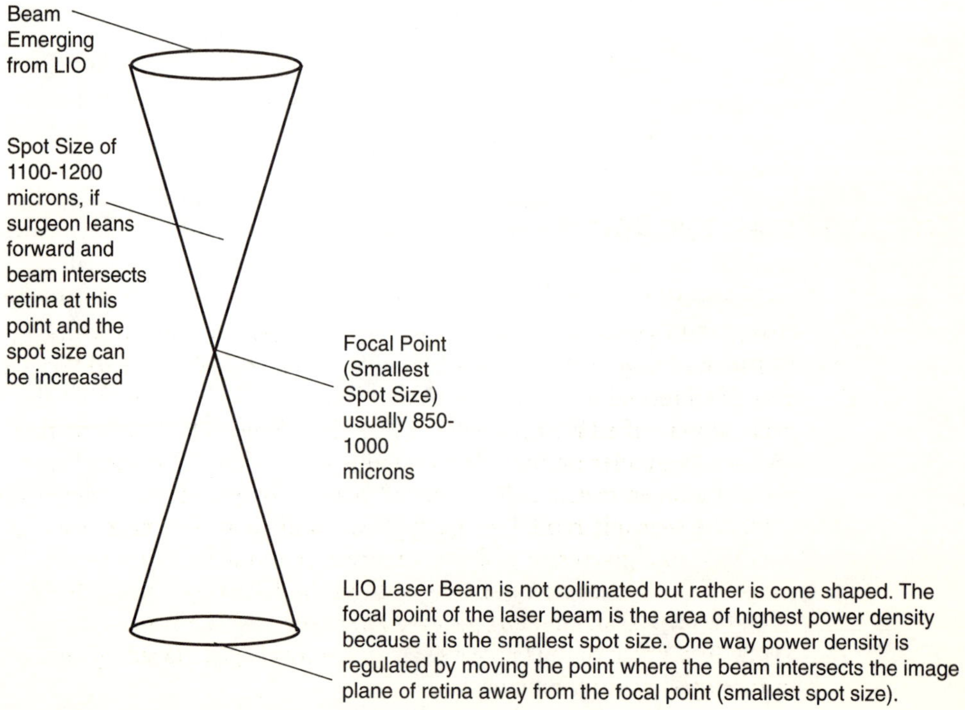

We recommend that one treat away from the focal point of the beam to allow room for slight forward and backward movement of the beam intersecting the retina. This is an easy way to titrate the power density by altering the spot size (the location of the beam intersecting the plane of the retina). This is especially useful in the peripheral retina where burn density can rapidly change as the retina thins.

Remember that:

The retinal spot size increases (↑) as the power of the hand-held condensing lens increases (↑)

The retinal spot size increases (↑) as the plus power of the refraction of the eye increases (↑)

Minus refraction (-) means decreased spot size

Plus refraction (+) means increased spot size.

EFFECT OF CONDENSING LENS ON LIO SPOT SIZE

For rough estimate of retinal spot size, use the Optic disc (1500 -1800 µ) and compare laser spot size to size of optic disc.

Spot Size at Image Plane X $\dfrac{\text{Power of Hand Held Lens}}{\text{Refractive Power of Average Eye}}$ = Spot Size at Retina

example 1: 900 µ (Spot Size at Image Plane) X $\dfrac{\text{20D (Power of Condensing Lens)}}{\text{60D (Refractive Power of Average Eye)}}$ = 300 µ Spot Size

example 2: 900 µ (Spot Size at Image Plane) X $\dfrac{\text{30D (Power of Condensing Lens)}}{\text{60D (Refractive Power of Average Eye)}}$ = 450 µ Spot Size

EFFECT OF REFRACTIVE STATUS ON LIO SPOT SIZE

Explanation

Compared to an emmetropic eye, a myopic retinal image appears magnified at the image plane. A laser spot of a given size will cover less of the magnified retinal image area of the myopic eye than it will on the relatively unmagnified retinal image of an emmetropic eye. Therefore, final spot size is smaller on the myopic fundus image than an identical spot placed on an emmetropic eye's retinal image. Compared to an emmetropic eye, a hyperopic retinal image appears minified at the image plane. A laser spot of a given size will cover more area of the minified retinal image of the hyperopic eye than it will on the relatively "unminified" retinal image of an emmetropic eye. Therefore, final spot size is larger on the hyperopic fundus image than an identical spot placed on an emmetropic eye's retina image.

Effect of Vitreous Substitutes on LIO Spot Size

Memorize what myopic (-) and hyperopic (+) refractive status does to spot size. Then view the retina with the vitreous substitute in place and decide if the substance renders the eye myopic or hyperopic. Then apply the rules for myopia or hyperopia to predict the spot size on the retina with a particuar vitreous substitute.

1. Air-myopic (decreased spot size)
2. Gas-myopic (decreased spot size)
3. Silicone-hyperopic (increased spot size)
4. Perfluorocarbon-liquid hyperopic (increased spot size)

Tips for Focusing Spot and Choosing Condensing Lenses

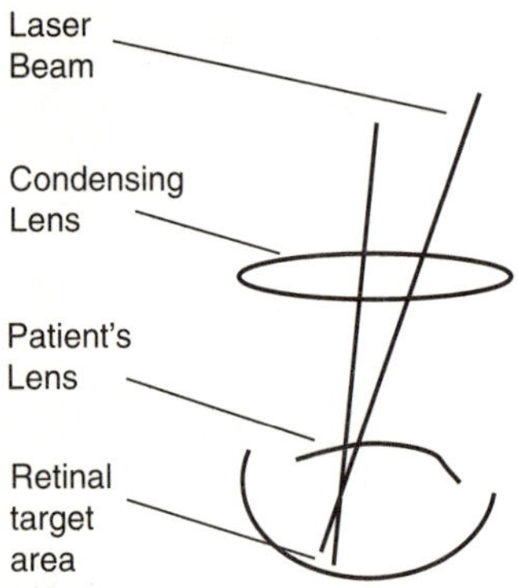

1. Line up three points of light
   a. Laser beam coming from indirect source
   b. Purkinke images of condensing lens
   c. Retinal target point
2. Use central two-thirds of condensing lens for ideal optical effect. Peripheral lens aberrations causes elliptical burns.
3. Use 28-D lens to magnify the spot size in highly myopic eyes or eyes rendered myopic by vitreous substitutes (phakic gas-filled eye).
4. Use 20- or 14-D lens to minify spot size in hyperopic eyes or eyes rendered hyperopic by vitreous substitutes (aphakic gas-filled eye, phakic silicone filled eye.).
5. Possible Techniques to Position Spots
   a. Move patient's eye with a scleral depressor to position image of peripheral retina into view
   b. Move retinal image with a prismatic (base in) effect of the hand-held condensing lens by tilting lens
   c. Move the aiming beam spot by gentle movement of the surgeon's head (least desirable since this causes neck fatigue)
   d. Use combination of all techniques (most commonly done)

COMPLICATIONS

Complications include macular burns (improper alignment and focusing); anterior segment burns (improper alignment and focusing) on cornea and lens; perforation of Bruch's membrane (improper power density) (Change condensing lens to make a larger burn–increase diopteric power of condensing lens–change intersection of retinal image away from the focal point of the laser beam by leaning forward or backward); vascular spasm, occlusion, or rupture (rare) (avoid treating over major retinal vessels); retinal hole (rare) (power density problem).

6 Transconjunctival Anterior Retinal Cryopexy

Indications, Techniques, and Complications

Indications

Indications to perform transconjunctivial anterior retinal cryopexy include

1. Treatment of peripheral retinal tears and holes
2. Treatment of some cases of proliferative Diabetic retinopathy
   a. Supplemental treatment for nonregressing neovascularization after laser treatment
   b. Treatment of eyes with media opacities that preclude laser treatment
   c. Treatment initially in settings wherein no laser is available
3. Treatment of Stage III (active) ROP
4. Treatment of Intermediate Uveitis (Pars Planitis)
5. Treatment of Laser nonresponsive Ischemic Central Retinal Vein Occlusion (CRVO)
6. Treatment of Laser nonresponsive Ischemic Ocular Syndrome (Carotoid Occlusive Disease)

Anesthesia

1. Topical Anesthesia (prior to retrobulbar)
2. Peribulbar (if monocular)
3. Retrobulbar
   Use a 50:50 mixture:
   0.75% Marcaine, 2.0% Xylocaine, 150 IU hyaluronidase (Wydase®)
4. General (occasional patient: this must be done in surgical suite)

20 And 28 diopter condensing lenses are needed. Other needed supplies are: lid speculum, balanced salt solution, topical anesthetic, and standard retinal cryoprobe. Note: Test the freezing capability of the probe prior to commencing patient treatment.

Treatment Intervals

Conduct one or more sessions at one to two week intervals. It is preferable to conduct two or more sessions if rubeosis is present. Overtreating in one session may increase intraocular inflammation, increase IOP and cause shallow choroidals.

Timing of Cryo Applications

To time cryo applications, place the probe 10 to 11 mm behind the limbus. Briefly touch the foot pedal. (This creates conjunctival adhesion.)

Bring the condensing lens into place. Depress with a probe–visualize the retina to be treated. Begin counting as the foot pedal is depressed. Note the time when the retinal whitening occurs.

PLACEMENT OF TRANSCONJUNCTIVAL CRYOPEXY FREEZING SPOTS IN EYES WITH PROLIFERATIVE RETINOPATHY.

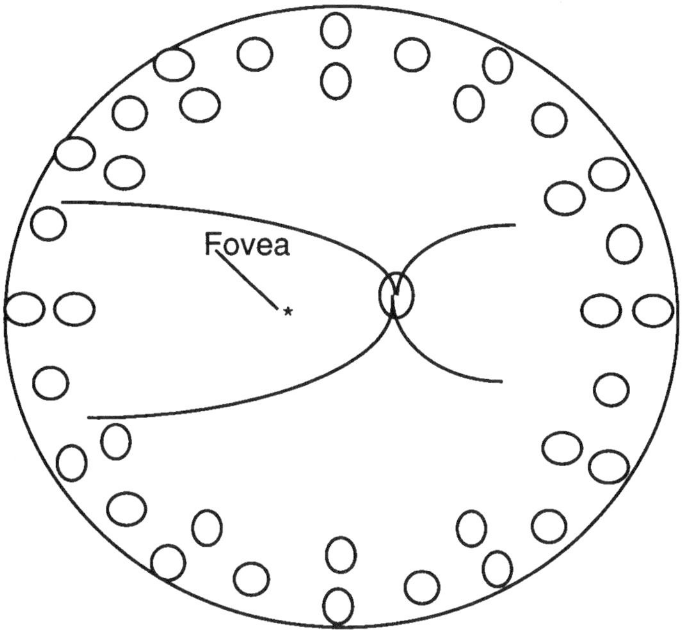

Two spots per clock hour and one spot per half-hour.

TECHNIQUE FOR ANTERIOR RETINAL CRYOTHERAPY FOR PROLIFERATIVE RETINOPATHY

The technique differs for ROP and retinal tears; see later. There are two freezes per clock hour, and one freeze per half hour. Do the posterior freeze first. Then, slide the probe anteriorly in the same clock hour and do the anterior one. Avoid treatment at 3:00 and 9:00 o'clock long posterior ciliary vessels and nerves. Avoid direct treatment over major retinal vessels. Treat the inferior retina first if possible. One may lose the inferior view if vitreous hemorrhage occurs and settles inferiorly following the initial treatment.

TREATMENT OF RETINAL TEARS

Perform the procedure in the office transconjunctivally, or in the OR transsclerally (conjuntiva taken down). Use a topical anesthesia. A peribulbar or retrobulbar injection to supplement may be necessary for pain. Peribulbar 1% lidocaine in the involved quadrant is recommended. Retrobulbar 1 to 2% lidocaine is useful but less often recommended, since the patient loses the ability to position the eye for visualization of the pathology. Use a retinal cryo probe as a scleral depressor. Locate tear/hole(s)–eye moves in the direction of the break. Visualize the treatment at all times. Surround break(s) completely with an adequate margin. Treat the edges but not directly over large tears. Create retinal whitening. Avoid overtreating. This disperses RPE cells and promotes proliferative vitreo retinopathy (PVR). Treat only the area(s) involved.

Technique for ROP Cryotherapy

The treatment is performed in a neonatal nursery or OR. Cardiopulmonary monitoring (for Bradycardia/Apnea) is required. Use a topical anesthesia. Use subconjunctival lidocaine (0.5 to 1.0%). Dilate with 2% homatropine and 2.5% phenylephrine given three, two and one hours prior to treatment. Use a standard retinal cryoprobe (The practitioner may use a cataract or newer neonatal probe.) Apply contiguous single spots of cryotherapy anterior to the fibrovascular ridge. The ridge itself should not be treated. Endpoint freeze occurs with sudden whitening of the retina. Treat an avascular retina for 360°. The number of applications range from 36 to 50.

Postoperative Care

Instill an antibiotic-steroid ointment prior to patching. Patch the eye, especially if retrobulbar anesthesia is given. Prescribe analgesic medication for three to five days. One day postoperatively, start topical steroids for three to seven days and cycloplegic drops for three to seven days.

Followup

Examine the patient for retinal holes or tears after seven to fourteen days, and for proliferative retinopathy or uveitis after seven to ten days, and at one, three and six months.

For ROP, examination is usually done seven to ten days after treatment and the patient is retreated as necessary until regression of ROP occurs; retreat if there are any skip areas or if persistent plus disease is associated with a segmental shallow RD in areas skipped, or progression of extraretinal fibrovascular proliferation contiguous with skipped areas. Only treat untreated areas in sector of activity. One, three and six months after stabilization of retina, check the patient again for ROP.

Complications

Complications include corneal freezing, lenticular freezing-cataract, serous choroidal detachment causing shallow anterior chamber, choroidal rupture (subretinal hemorrhage or subretinal membrane, later), retinal vascular bleed (ruptured vessel), loss of accommodation (ciliary nerves), vitreous contraction with subsequent tractional retinal detachment, postoperative pressure spike, or exacerabated inflammation or IOP in eyes with rubeosis or glaucoma.

Key Points

Adequate anesthesia is imperative. Visualization and timing of freezes (if possible) are important. Avoid freezing the retinal vessels or choroidal nerves. Give adequate postoperative analgesia. Avoid excessive treatment in rubeotic eyes, i.e., do one to two quadrants only per session so that less inflammation will be created in each session.